W9-ARK-268

# Vince Lombardi

# Vince Lombardi

Academic Industries, Inc.
West Haven, Connecticut 06516

*ISBN 0-88301-790-3*

*Published by*
Academic Industries, Inc.
The Academic Building
Saw Mill Road
West Haven, Connecticut 06516

Printed in the United States of America

# Vince Lombardi

## Contents

·VINCE LOMBARDI·
Vince Lombardi is perhaps the best-known coach in the history of professional football.
31
20
As head coach of the Green Bay Packers, Vince Lombardi made a winning team out of one that was used to losing. By 1961, the Packers were champions.
Vincent Thomas Lombardi grew up in Brooklyn, New York. His parents were from Italy.
Thank you, Lord, for what we are about to receive . . .

# On Both Sides of the Teacher's Desk

For a while, young Vincent studied to become a priest.
But by the time he was ready for college at Fordham University in New York City, football was a big part of his life.
He was well known by many teams Fordham played because he was so strong.
He was not a star, but he was a good player. Even then his teammates looked up to him.
I pray we'll win!
Never pray to win a game. Pray to do your best.
Vincent was a good student, too. In 1936 he finished college, earning high honors.
Good work!
Thank you, sir!

Vince was too small to become a professional football player. So he went to law school.
When he finished law school, he went to work in an office. One day an ex-teammate called his mother.
Mrs. Lombardi, I'd like to talk to Vince about coming to coach for me at St. Cecelia's.
Vince's mother was shocked.
Coach football! But he *has* a good job!
But Vince was very interested.
The job pays only $1,700 a year, and you'll have to coach basketball and teach, too.
Great! I'll take the job.

Vince had never played or coached basketball before, but soon St. Cecelia's had winning teams.
Great job, Vince. We'll be state champions this year for sure!
Thank you, sir. I hope so!
But football was always Vince's game. In those days there were no tackling sleds to help players practice blocking. Instead, they had to take on Vince.
Okay, Joe, hit me!
Sure, Coach.
Vince was always kind to his boys whether in the classroom or on the football field.
What's the matter, Joe? You look tired.

*Vince loved football more than anything. After work, he and his friends would set up some cans and plan trick plays.*

I'll move this end over to the side.
Okay, I'll send in this tackle.

That was play. But back at school, Vince was all work.
Anyone who hasn't learned his plays by tomorrow is off the team.
Vince was hard, but he was fair. And all his work paid off.
Great job, Vince! Looks like you'll be state champions again!
Thanks, Father.
27
In eight seasons, Lombardi's football teams were state champions six times.

# The Professional Coach

His team was known all around New Jersey. Everyone loved Vince.
Vince, I like the way you make winners. I'll pay you $15,000 a year to take charge of the men who work for my construction company.
That's a good offer, but I just couldn't give up football.
In 1947, Vince took the job as assistant coach at Fordham University.
If you play for me, you play hard. But play clean, understand?
Then, in 1949, Vince went to work for Earl Blaik at the United States Military Academy in West Point, New York.
Welcome, Vince. I know you'll do well here.
Thanks, sir. I'll do my best.

These were important years for Vince. Earl Blaik was a great coach. Vince learned a great deal.
You're doing a fine job with these guys, Vince. It's good to have you on the team.
I'm just glad to be able to work with you, sir.
72
15
A
Earl Blaik was one of the first coaches who used movies to help his team.
This Navy team is weak on its left side.
I'll make sure our Army boys are ready to make use of it.
We won! You were right again, sir.
Just remember, Vince, inches make champions.

Army had one of the great college football teams in the country. Then, in 1951, most of the team was caught cheating in the classroom. All of them were thrown out of school.
This is terrible. We don't have any experienced players.
Don't worry, we can build a new team.
COACH
74
That year Army lost to Navy. The score was 42 to 7.
Vince, I won't blame you if you take another job.
What? We're going to be on top again next year.
I expect extra work from everyone! Remember, inches make champions.
18

In 1953, Army made a great comeback. Once again they were a top team. Everyone thought Vince Lombardi would get the job of head coach at a top college.

*That job never came. Vince was unhappy. He decided to accept a job as assistant coach for the New York Giants. He had never coached professional players before.*
Welcome to the New York Giants, Vince. We're putting you in charge of our offensive team.
*In 1953, the Giants had won only one game. Frank Gifford was a new player that year.*
Vince, this is Frank Gifford.
Glad to meet you, Coach.
Don't speak too soon, Frank. You are my half-back. You're going to work hard.
You guys are lazy! I want to see some action out there!

*These, too, were important learning years for Vince Lombardi. He had coached high school and college boys. Now he had to learn how to work with older men.*

Vince Lombardi was a man who knew what he wanted.
Okay, that's today's play. Let's go out and do it.
At first, some of the players didn't like Vince. He always wanted them to work harder.
Once again, gentlemen! If it takes all day and all night, we're going to do this until you get it right!
But slowly they saw that Vince was a man who only asked others to give what he expected from himself. He was on the job at all hours.
Well, do you think that play we did today will work?
Sure, Coach. We can do it for you.

The players and the rest of the world soon saw that Lombardi knew what he was doing.
The Giants became a strong team. In 1956, Frank Gifford was voted the Most Valuable Player in the National Football League. And the Giants won the championship.
We're proud of you, Vince.
I'm proud, too. But I'd really like to be head coach.
We want to keep Jim Lee Howell as head coach for another year. But then the job is yours!
There's nothing I want more.

# With the Green Bay Packers

In 1957, the Giants did well again. But still Vince didn't get the head coaching job.
The News
LOMBARDI GOES TO GREEN BAY

*The Giants were the best team in the league. The Green Bay Packers were the worst team. They hadn't had a winning season in fifteen years. But when they offered Vince the job as head coach, he jumped at the chance.*

I'm proud that I was asked. You know I'll give it my best. But . . .

. . . don't expect miracles. You know, we're starting at the bottom!
Vince was forty-six years old. This was his big chance, but it might also be his last one.

Now Vince was running the show. First he studied movies of the players he had to work with.
He learned his players' weak points and their strong points. Then he hired four assistant coaches.
Phil Bengston, meet Norb Hecker.
It's good to be here.
I expect the best from all of you. I don't like mistakes, and I accept no excuses.

The Packers worked day and night. From the start, Vince let everyone know that he meant business.
Coach, do you think I could get off before nine o'clock tonight? I'd like to do some Christmas shopping.
Do you want to be Santa Claus, or do you want to be a football coach? There's no room for both!
When Vince came to Green Bay, he brought one player with him—Emlen Tunnell.
It's good to see you, Vince.
It's good to see you, Emlen. You know, I'm going to build a dynasty here.
When the spring training camp for players opened, Vince let everyone know what he had in mind.
You're here for one reason—you're here to win. I'm here for one reason—I'm here to make sure you don't forget it.
31

Vince Lombardi made many players into stars. One of them was Paul Hornung.
I've been looking at the films, Paul. You've been playing quarter-back and halfback. If you want to play for me, you're going to play halfback—or not play at all!
Okay, Coach. I was ready to quit this team, but I'll try it your way.
Vince turned the unhappy player into a great star. Three years later, in 1960, Paul Hornung scored 176 points, breaking all records. This record still stands today.

*Another unhappy player was Bart Starr. He had been with the Packers since 1956, but he had spent most of his time on the bench.*

Thanks to Vince Lombardi, Starr would become one of the best-known quarterbacks of all time.
20
15

I think you can really help this team, Bart. I'm going to give you the chance you never had.
Thanks, Coach.
15

*For ten years, Bart Starr would lead the league in passing. Other quarterbacks had better single seasons, but no one had a better overall record. In six National Football League Championships, Bart threw 145 passes and had only one interception, a record many people find hard to believe.*

15
71
24

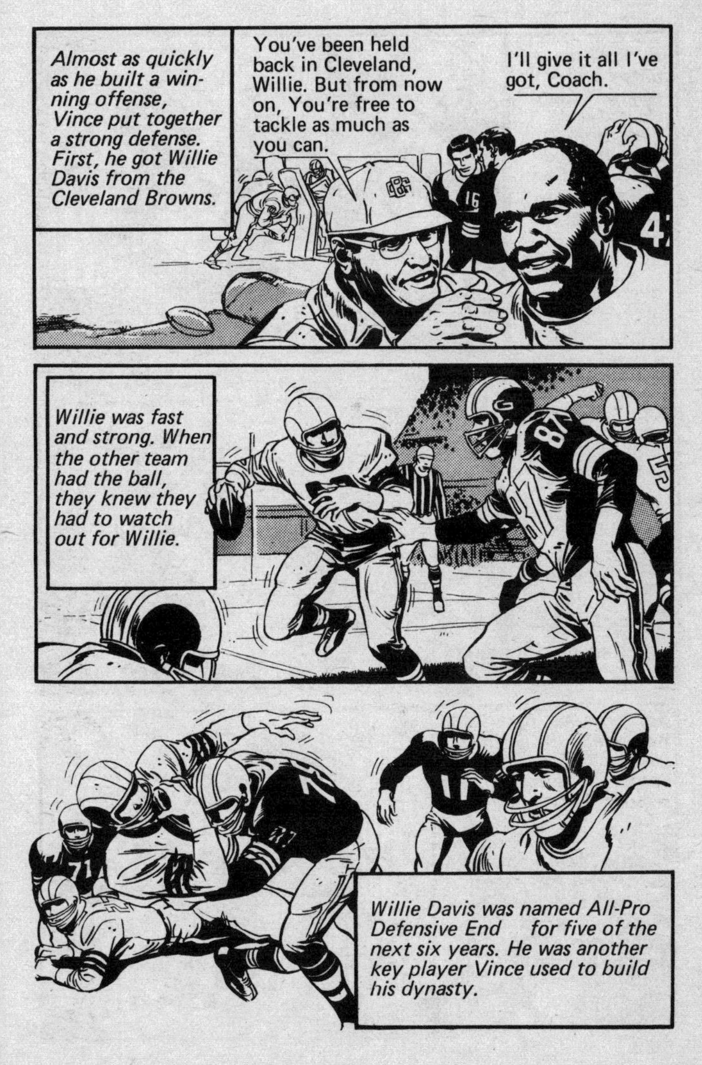
Almost as quickly as he built a winning offense, Vince put together a strong defense. First, he got Willie Davis from the Cleveland Browns.
You've been held back in Cleveland, Willie. But from now on, You're free to tackle as much as you can.
I'll give it all I've got, Coach.
Willie was fast and strong. When the other team had the ball, they knew they had to watch out for Willie.
Willie Davis was named All-Pro Defensive End for five of the next six years. He was another key player Vince used to build his dynasty.

*Another important player on defense was Henry Jordan. For five straight years, Henry was an All-Pro defensive tackle.*

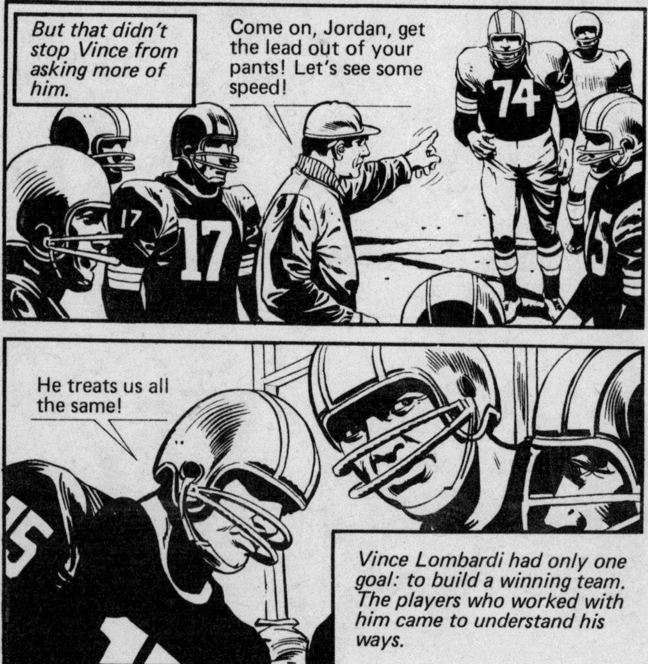
But that didn't stop Vince from asking more of him.
Come on, Jordan, get the lead out of your pants! Let's see some speed!
He treats us all the same!
Vince Lombardi had only one goal: to build a winning team. The players who worked with him came to understand his ways.

From the first day of summer practice camp, Lombardi took charge of every minute of his players' lives.
You guys are all pros, or you wouldn't be here. This team is going to the top. Sometimes you will hate me, but if you want to stay with this team, you'll do as I say.
To start with, I'm going to fine anyone who isn't in bed by eleven o'clock.
That night Emlen Tunnell walked into the dormitory at one minute to eleven.
That will cost you fifty dollars.

Man, it's not eleven o'clock yet.
Emlen, you know you can't be in bed with your clothes off in one minute!
They both laughed. But Emlen had to pay the fifty dollars.
During that same training camp, Vince let everyone know they had to be in top shape to play on his team.
You guys are all too heavy. Lose twenty pounds each in two weeks, or you're off the team.
The players thought he was crazy, but they soon found out differently. Two weeks later Jerry Helluin was sent home.
I thought he was kidding.
Sorry, Jerry, Vince Lombardi means business!

In spite of their problems, Vince pulled the team together quickly.
In those days, professional football teams played twelve games each season. The Green Bay Packers had won fewer than half their games during the past fifteen years. But in 1959, Vince's first year, they won seven, lost five, and placed third in the league.

But Vince kept asking for more.
Last year we did great; this year we're going to do better. No one can beat you out there—no one except yourselves. Let's go!

In 1960, Vince's second season, the Packers won the Western Division Championship. It was a great moment for Vince Lombardi. But it was just the beginning.

Before every game Vince called the team together for a prayer.
Thank you, Lord .
They never prayed to win. They prayed only to do their best.
In 1961, the Green Bay Packers went to the top. They won the National Football League Championship. The next year Vince's picture appeared on the cover of Time magazine.
THE SPORT OF THE '60s
TIME
In 1962, the Packers made it two championships in a row. This time they defeated the New York Giants, the team for which Vince had once been assistant coach.

Vince wanted to win three championships in a row. But in 1963 and 1964, many of his players were injured. Still, the team placed second in each of those years.
12
75
80
Then in 1965, the Packers came back even stronger.
69
61
17
87
They won the league championship in 1965 and again in 1967. The Green Bay Packers were the most famous team, and Vince Lombardi was the most famous coach in the history of professional football.

# The Man Who Could Not Retire

Then Vince did what no other coach had ever done. He decided to retire while he was still on top.
But he loved football too much to stay away.
So in 1969, he went back to work as head coach for the Washington Redskins.
This team has been a loser for years. Well, all that's past. We're going to work, and we're going to win.
The Redskins finished second in the league during Vince's first year.

Vince said they'd be the champions the next year. Many other people agreed with him. But in the summer of 1970, Vince Lombardi was found to have cancer. He died soon afterward.
I just can't believe it!
God must be in a lot of trouble if he needs Vince Lombardi up there.
The End

## Do you remember?

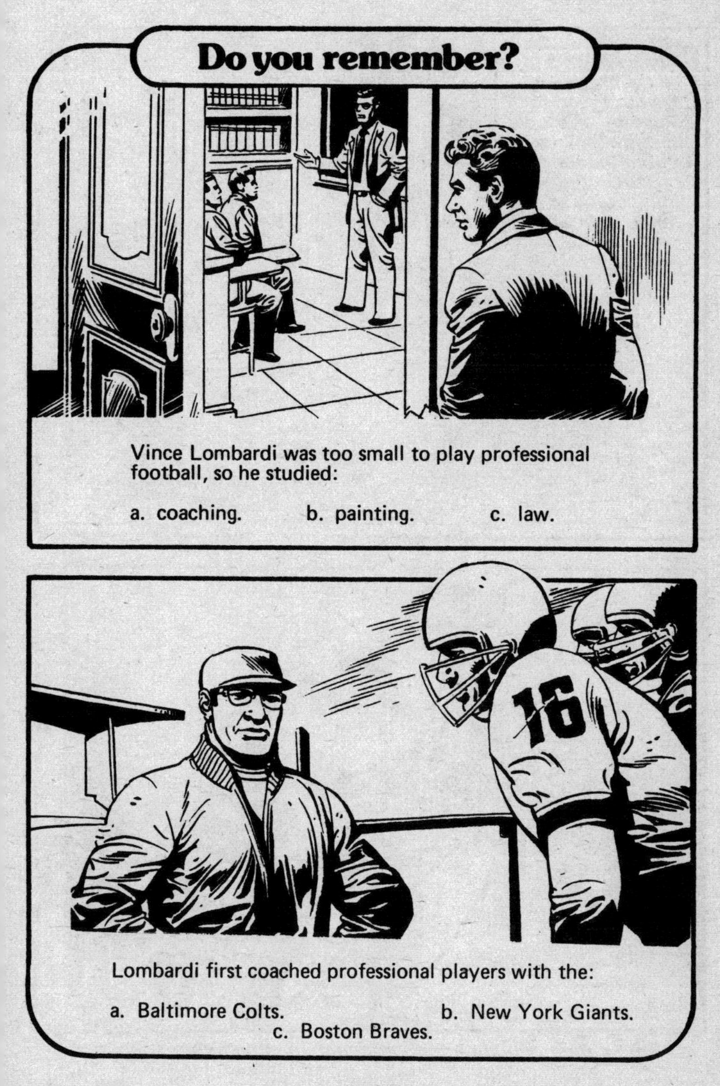
16

Vince Lombardi was too small to play professional football, so he studied:

a. coaching. b. painting. c. law.

Lombardi first coached professional players with the:

a. Baltimore Colts. b. New York Giants. c. Boston Braves.

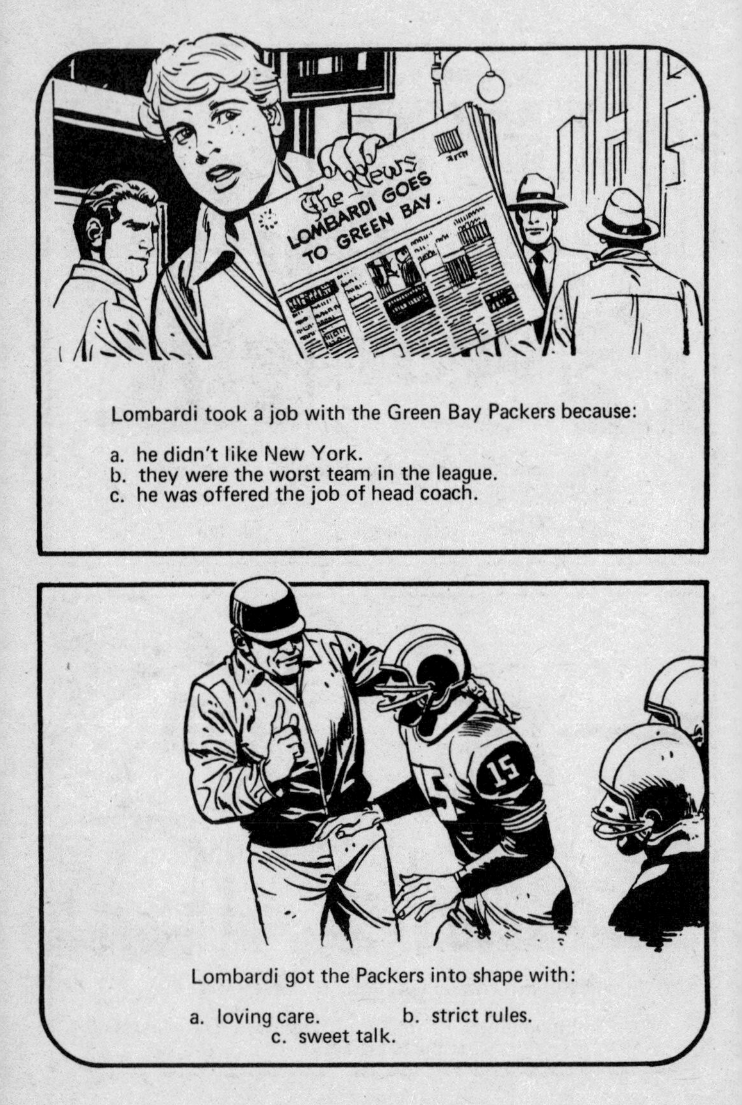
The News
LOMBARDI GOES TO GREEN BAY.
15

Lombardi took a job with the Green Bay Packers because:

a. he didn't like New York.
b. they were the worst team in the league.
c. he was offered the job of head coach.

Lombardi got the Packers into shape with:

a. loving care.
b. strict rules.
c. sweet talk.

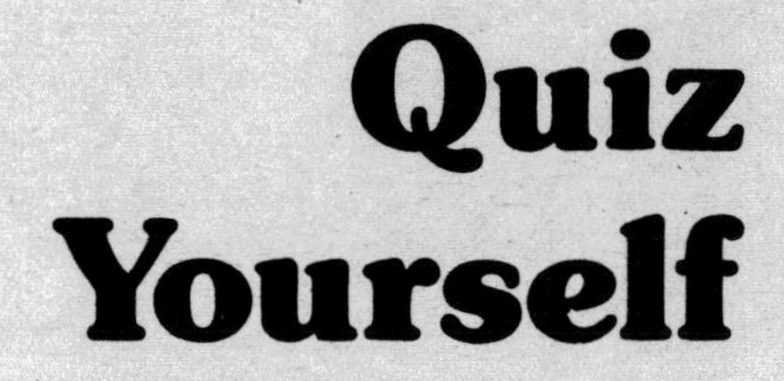
Quiz
Yourself

(Answers at end of section)

# Words to know

| | |
|---|---|
| champions | teams that win first place in leagues or contests |
| coach | a teacher or trainer of teams in various sports |
| league | a group of teams that play games against each other |
| retire | to stop working at one's job |
| professional athlete | a person who is paid for taking part in sports events |

# Can you use them?

*Using the words above, complete the following sentences.*

1. The Pittsburgh Steelers have often been the NFL ______________, the best team in their league.
2. A football player who plays for the Green Bay Packers is a ______________. He is paid for playing football.
3. Vince Lombardi was a famous football ______________ who trained many famous teams.
4. Most people keep busy with hobbies or other interests after they ____________.
5. Teams that play each other must all be in the same ______________.

## Using pictures

In reading illustrated stories, you will find it helpful to "read" the pictures as well as the words. Look at this picture. It shows us that football players learn about playing football in a classroom. The coach has drawn several plays on a blackboard. Now look at the middle picture on page 11 in the storybook and find another way in which coaches train their players.

## While you are reading

Vince Lombardi was a very strict trainer and coach. He demanded a lot from his men. While you are reading, make a list of some of the things he did to his men that show how strict he was.

# How well did you read?

*When you have finished reading, answer the following questions.*

1. Why did Vince Lombardi leave college coaching and start to work with professional football teams?

   (Check the correct answer.)

   _____ a. The college refused to give him more money.

   _____ b. The college fired him because his team had had a losing season.

   _____ c. He was finally offered a job as head coach of the New York Giants' offensive team.

   _____ d. He wanted to become famous.

The News
LOMBARDI GOES
TO GREEN BAY

2. What things made Vince Lombardi a good coach?

   (Check the correct *answers.*)

74

   _____ a. He used movies to study the way his men played.

   _____ b. He prayed to win before each game.

   _____ c. He treated all his men fairly.

   _____ d. He paid his men extra if they did well.

   _____ e. He always told his men that they could do better.

3. What does the saying "Inches make champions" mean?

(Check the correct answer.)

______ a. Taller players have a better chance of winning.

______ b. Players must keep their weight down in order to be champions.

______ c. Champions are always inches from the top.

______ d. A team might only have to be a little bit better to win.

4. Which of the following are men who became famous because of Vince Lombardi's coaching?

(Check the correct *answers.*)

______ a. Emlen Tunnell

______ b. Willie Davis

______ c. Joe Namath

______ d. Paul Hornung

______ e. Henry Jordan

______ f. Bart Starr

20
15

5. What did Vince find so challenging about coaching the Washington Redskins?

(Check the correct answer.)

_____ a. The players were known as troublemakers, and Vince thought he could change them with his strict rules.

_____ b. The team was a loser, and Vince thought he could build a winning team.

_____ c. The Redskins had no money, and Vince thought he could increase the number of fans who attended the games.

_____ d. The players were young and knew little about professional football.

## Using what you've read

Vince Lombardi was a very strict coach. If you walked into the locker room of one of his teams, you'd probably find a list of rules hanging on the wall. One rule might be "All men must be in bed by 11:00 PM or pay a fine." What are some other rules you'd expect to find on his list? Name five of them.

16

# ANSWER KEY

## VINCE LOMBARDI

### Can you use them?

1. champions
2. professional athlete
3. coach
4. retire
5. league

### How well did you read?

1. c
2. a, c, e
3. d
4. a, b, d, e, f
5. b

## COMPLETE LIST OF POCKET CLASSICS AVAILABLE

CLASSICS

C 1 Black Beauty
C 2 The Call of the Wild
C 3 Dr. Jekyll and Mr. Hyde
C 4 Dracula
C 5 Frankenstein
C 6 Huckleberry Finn
C 7 Moby Dick
C 8 The Red Badge of Courage
C 9 The Time Machine
C10 Tom Sawyer
C11 Treasure Island
C12 20,000 Leagues Under the Sea
C13 The Great Adventures of Sherlock Holmes
C14 Gulliver's Travels
C15 The Hunchback of Notre Dame
C16 The Invisible Man
C17 Journey to the Center of the Earth
C18 Kidnapped
C19 The Mysterious Island
C20 The Scarlet Letter
C21 The Story of My Life
C22 A Tale of Two Cities
C23 The Three Musketeers
C24 The War of the Worlds
C25 Around the World in Eighty Days
C26 Captains Courageous
C27 A Connecticut Yankee in King Arthur's Court
C28 The Hound of the Baskervilles
C29 The House of the Seven Gables
C30 Jane Eyre

COMPLETE LIST OF POCKET CLASSICS AVAILABLE (cont'd)

C31 The Last of the Mohicans
C32 The Best of O. Henry
C33 The Best of Poe
C34 Two Years Before the Mast
C35 White Fang
C36 Wuthering Heights
C37 Ben Hur
C38 A Christmas Carol
C39 The Food of the Gods
C40 Ivanhoe
C41 The Man in the Iron Mask
C42 The Prince and the Pauper
C43 The Prisoner of Zenda
C44 The Return of the Native
C45 Robinson Crusoe
C46 The Scarlet Pimpernel
C47 The Sea Wolf
C48 The Swiss Family Robinson
C49 Billy Budd
C50 Crime and Punishment
C51 Don Quixote
C52 Great Expectations
C53 Heidi
C54 The Illiad
C55 Lord Jim
C56 The Mutiny on Board H.M.S. Bounty
C57 The Odyssey
C58 Oliver Twist
C59 Pride and Prejudice
C60 The Turn of the Screw

## COMPLETE LIST OF POCKET CLASSICS AVAILABLE (cont'd)

### SHAKESPEARE

S 1 As You Like It
S 2 Hamlet
S 3 Julius Caesar
S 4 King Lear
S 5 Macbeth
S 6 The Merchant of Venice
S 7 A Midsummer Night's Dream
S 8 Othello
S 9 Romeo and Juliet
S10 The Taming of the Shrew
S11 The Tempest
S12 Twelfth Night

COMPLETE LIST OF POCKET CLASSICS AVAILABLE (cont'd)

BIOGRAPHIES

B 1 Charles Lindbergh
B 2 Amelia Earhart
B 3 Houdini
B 4 Walt Disney
B 5 Davy Crockett
B 6 Daniel Boone
B 7 Elvis Presley
B 8 The Beatles
B 9 Benjamin Franklin
B10 Martin Luther King, Jr.
B11 Abraham Lincoln
B12 Franklin D. Roosevelt
B13 George Washington
B14 Thomas Jefferson
B15 Madame Curie
B16 Albert Einstein
B17 Thomas Edison
B18 Alexander Graham Bell
B19 Vince Lombardi
B20 Pelé
B21 Babe Ruth
B22 Jackie Robinson
B23 Jim Thorpe
B24 Althea Gibson